9-18-99 - A beautiful fall day. But, we stayed put and rested after having had such a busy week.

We watched football and Miss America Pagent. I missed it last year.

9-19-99 Moved on to Indian Lakes Park at Batesville In. We will stay here til 10-3-99 then go back to Muncie In for kite fly.

9-20-99 A Cloudy day but, we did get out and take a hike in woods. Getting back on our walking schedule.

9-21-99 A much cooler day today. We drove to Greensburg In. I purchased a new iron. I fought with that other one long enough.

9-22-99 Max worked on kite lines today.

I did some paper work and took my walk. I'm seemingly keeping my sugar under control.

9-23-99 - We picked up our business cards from post office today. Richard Berkey had sent them. They were nice.

Found a meat store. It had all kinds of good meat. Made you want to try everything.

We came home & Max worked on kite lines. I struggled at the laundry. With 2 out of the 4 dryers not working it made for a long day there.

9-24-99 Drove to Metomora In, an old town on a canal. Lots of crafty shops there.

9-25-99 - I'm having some problems. Maybe my sugar is to low.

At times I'm having spasmatic pain in left Side. & hot flashes.

Might have to call Dr. Mellin.

9-26-99 - Beautiful fall days - Max was flying kites this morn & I'm trying to take care of my pain problems. Doing better I flew kites this PM.

People watched on sidelines.

Finally got to talk to Terry tonight.

9-27-99 - This was a day that it took us all day to get it done - Well not quite. We needed to get Elle's b-present in mail. We drove to Greensburg In. Bought gift & did some other things. Went to post office in Batesville In. wrapped it in parking lot at post office & got it in mail.

9-28-99 Stayed put today. Max repaired kite. I cleaned bathroom woodwork. Also cross stitched. We did our walking also. Doing it more regular now.

9-29-99 It rained all day. That was very much needed.

We stayed put.

Max caught up on his reading. I did cross stitch. I'm getting to place I want to get this kite picture done.

9-30-99 - This was trailer washing day. From top to bottom.

I worked on books. Then I washed window and polished black around bottom of trailer. It's looking good.

10-1-99 - Another work day, groceries, laundry wash truck & truck windows. That's about enough of that for awhile.

10-2-99 - Finished up our work projects and watched football rest of day.

10-3-99 - Moved to Muncie to the Aeronautical Academy of Aviation. for This is site of International Kite Festival. Lots of flying area. Don't know what to expect. But ready for fun.

The weather is changing. We have wind but its colder. The wind blew all night.

With no hook ups it will be challenging.

10-4-99 It was only 45° when I got up at 8:00 this morning.

10-4-99 A cold Oct morn in Oct and drizzly rain. Not a good way to start kite festival.

We gave coffee to some workers setting up tents.

Stayed put til after lunch then went to convention center to register.

We stayed there til the dinner. Checked out our packets etc. They had a raffle after dinner. We didn't win anything.

Came back to Trailer and planned out our day for Tues.

Went to bed. & got warm.

10-5-99 - We both went to applique class this morning. Charlie Dunton really knew what he was talking about. Watched mass ascencion at 1:00. Then we walked around and oohed & ahed over peoples kites. Took in annual business meeting of AKA.

10-6-99 Went to class with Kathy Goodwin on fittings.

Came back to field and had lunch. and watched Stars sport kite competition. So many good kites

Went downtown town to a night fly. The lighted kites in the sky was awesome. 10-7-99 - We were suppose to be at a class at 10:30. It was to be at fly field. Never found it. So we looked around.

At 1:00 was the mass ascencion for sport fighter kites. Then the big moment arrived. Max was to show his kite. He had plenty of wind and could use his tail. I named it Freedom Flyer This was his red, white & blue one. It did very well. There were 7 others participating in this class.

There were about 6-8 judges.

We taken pictures of the other kites & of the judges.

All in all he felt

very good about his
showing.

We won't find the
results til Sat. night
at the awards banquet.
We feel good about the
whole competition.

This evening we went
to convention center
to watch indoor
flying.

Also took in the
miniature kite gallery
and the fly market.
Came home unwound.
We were tired. Only
2 more full days to go.

10-8-99 - It was, windy, wet,
and miserable today.
We stayed in and watched
the people fly kites
in the rain. Yes the
competition goes on
rain or shine.
They had the mass
ascension of soft
parasails at one o'clock.
We watched from

the window.

This evening was dinner and the auction at convention center. It was a silent auction and also a bidding auction.

Max got a T-shirt in silent auction.

I didn't get what I bid on.

It was all fun.

10-9-99 - Today is last day of Kite convention. It's still raining.

We went to an applique class at 9:00 A.M. It was really informative. We came back to trailer & had lunch.

Pat & Kevin Smith had come from Elkhart to see the Kites etc. We got them dried out in trailer as we watched from inside the final mass ascension & banner parade.

They then left and we took it easy the rest of afternoon. About 5:30 we went to convention center for cocktails, dinner and awards ceremony. We were hoping Max would have a chance in novice kite builders. There was approx 36 people in his category. They gave awards for 1st, 2nd & 3rd. He didn't get an award. We were proud that he had tried and we felt he had done well.

Got home about 11:30 PM.

10-10-99 - Slept in this morning.

Finally got around because we were moving to Horseshoe Lakes at St Bernice In

We had survived with our batteries and

holding tank this week of no utilities. I hope we don't do it again for a long time. Spaces were few at Horseshoe Lakes but we did find a site with sewer.

10-11-99 After sleeping in and taking it easy this morning, We took a long walk in the park. Our beautiful fall weather has returned.

10-12-99 A trip to the big metropolis of St Bernice for a ton of mail. Then on to Terre Haute. We shipped the stepping stones to Terry's house. did some other shopping and had lunch at Applebys.

Then we came home and I worked on mail

10-13-99 - Sunny but windy. May flew his revolution kite. I did laundry

10-14-99 - Moving day -
200 miles today. We
left Indiana and
drove to the other
side of ~~then~~ St Louis Mo.
We took interstate all
the way.
Stayed at a Good Sam
Park. Pin Oak RV Pk -
Very nice park.
Max's filing is completely
out now.

10-15-99 - Groceries was
at the top of the list
today. Seems we were
out of everything.
Found a Walmart Super
Center and took care of
that.
Then we went to an
Italian Restaurant
recommended by campground
manager. Very good.

10-16-99 Moved on to Mt
Vernon Mo. Parked
right at hearing aid
clinic. Max has appoint-
ment for on Monday

We got in early PM and just stayed put the rest of the day. Watched football & baseball playoffs.

10-17-99 We went out to breakfast this morn. Not many choices in town of 3700 people. But, found a place. We came back and watched car race, baseball playoffs and football. The one baseball game went 5 hrs.

10-18-99 This was Max's hearing aid appointment day. at 9:00 AM. That's early. But, we made it O.K.

Got his hearing test and decided which of their aids he would get. We took the best they had and they were computerized to his test. We left, went back to trailer, had lunch, and took a nap.

At 2:00PM we went back for the fitting.

Everything seems OK so far.

10-19-99 We're moving today. We went to Bass Master Pro Shop at Springfield Mo.

Max wanted to see this place.

What a place! They have everything sporting wise you could want.

We left there about 1:00 and moved on to the Turkey Creek Village, an Escape Park at Hollister Mo. This is just outside of Branson, Mo.

We had to boondock the 1st night but we'd get a full hook up spot tomorrow. After setting up we made a trip to Post Office. Got a hair appoint for tomorrow. Really need it bad.

Then, we drove into Branson to look at all the changes. Wow! This place has grown. We were held in 87 + 92.

It is my birthday today. We ate at Out Back Steak House. Very good!

We came back and I did paper work this evening.

10-20-99 Moved to a full hook up spot this morn. Had lunch at club house and got our hair cut this PM.

We came back and rested a bit and went to the first of four shows we were going to see.

We saw Bobby Vinton and the Glen Miller Orchestra. Good show, lots of oldies.

10-21-99 Another beautiful fall day.

I worked on paper work this morning.

At 3:00 today we went to Yakov Smirnoff Show. He's quite a comedian. I bought book & tape from his show.

Stopped at Schlotskys Deli for supper.

We like those sandwiches. Came home and relaxed rest of evening.

10-22-99 - We were out and on the go bright and early this morning. First stop was post office then to a 10:00 show. I opened mail from Terry and family before we went to show.

It was my birthday things.

Jon & Elle sent me a neat package that looked like a bag of pretzels. Really it was jig saw puzzle that had pretzels all over it.

After show we went to a restaurant called McGuffies. It was patterned after a school and had McGuffy Readers for menus.

My grandfather had been a school teacher and read me stories from the McGuffy reader.

After lunch we took in 2 craft type malls. I got some stickers & paper for my picture books.

Came home tired and stayed put for evening.

10-22-99 - The show we saw this morning was a man with no arms. He played guitar with his feet. Quite an insperational show.

10-23-99 - We went to breakfast at campground.
Took a walk and came
back and stayed put
for the day.
The World Series started
tonight. The Yankees
won!
Have to call tomorrow
and get my bet with
Terry.
10-24-99 - Still stayed put
today. Watched football
and world series. Yankees
won again.
Talked to both Sue & Terry.
Went to ice cream social
at park.
10-25-99 - Went shopping
for a new piece of luggage
today. We wanted one
that had wheels attached.
Found one at outlett mall.
Came home to see if
it would fit under
bed. That was OK.
Then we went to
Country Tonite Show

in afternoon.
We went to Peppercorn
Restaurant afterwards.
Came home and checked
messages. We had 7
messages. They were all
from Sue and they
started at 1:00 A.M.
Tim had had a heart
attack and was in
hospital.
We were to call about
9:00 P.M.
Terry had come down
to help her out.
Things were as good
as they could be at
this point.
Terry will stay couple
days.
Tim will be in
hospital till at least
Fri.
10-26-99 Did laundry &
cleaned trailer today.
Max was getting around
and found we had a
trailer tire going down.

Took it off, found a nail.
He took it and got it
fixed. Sure were glad
we weren't on road.
Talked to Sue this evening.
Things seem to be doing
better with Tim.
Terry is helping her.
Also, Yankees won
again. Its now 3-0.
They can win it all
tomorrow.

10-27-99-
Moving day - a long move
to boot.
Very pretty drive from
Branson to North Arkansas.
through the hills.
After Little Rock Rte 30
was very rough.
We stopped at De Gray
State Park at Arkadelphia
Ar. Beautiful park on
Lake De Gray.
Took a long walk after
settling up.
Checked in on Tim.
He's progressing good

Yankee's won Series Tonight.

Terry is upset.

He will leave in morning.

10-28-99 - We just explored the park today and enjoyed one more nice fall day.

10-29-99 We moved on to Oakwood Texas today. We took a state route instead of Interstate. Much better roads. We arrived about 4:00 PM We are next to highway. Last night there was a major accident. A head on collision.

They evacuated one lady by helicopter. They landed on the campground property. Police cars & ambulances all over the place. Bad!

10-30-99 It rained all day.

We did make a trip

to Palestine TX to a Walmart.

Came home, stayed put and watched our Saturday sports.

10-31-99 Another leisure day. We stayed put.

11-1-99 - Moved on to Columbus Texas. This is a TT park and we've been here before. Nice quiet park in the pecan grove. We like it here.

11-2-99 Stayed put today Max went to pond and did some fishing. Even caught some.

We will have them tomorrow.

I worked on picture book & x-stitch.

I'm still putting pictures in from kite festival. I'll catch up some day.

11-3-99 Today was kind of a repeat of yesterday Max fished, I worked

on picture book.
not done yet.

We ate the fish
Max caught. Tasted
pretty good. Haven't
had blue gill in many
a moon.

11-4-99 - We drove to
Brenham Tx today.
A neat old town. Ate
at a restaurant that we
were at before, when in
the area.

Came back, Max got
more bait, He went
fishing but not good
today. He threw the
few back he caught.
I did my thing and
worked some more
on picture book - Not
done yet.

11-5-99 - Went to our
favorite German Restaurant
tonight. Its about 10 miles
from campground in the
country.

They've changed owners.

Also they have expanded.
They had a 3 piece band.
They were better than
the other band.
They played the German
music but also a
variety of music.
We came back and
called See. Tim was
back in hospital.
He is doing better
and hopefully coming
home tomorrow.
11-6-94 - Walked to lodge
for breakfast.
Went grocery shopping.
Came back fixed lunch
from leftovers from night
before at German Restaurant
Watched the Saturday football
games. At 5:00 we went
to dinner at lodge.
Had baked chicken.
Didn't cook anything today.
11-7-99 - Max tried his
luck at fishing again
today. He did catch
1 nice, really nice

blue gill. Along
with a few small ones.
Then he got 2 turtles,
that was a story within
itself.

Talked to Sue. She's
pretty down. With Tim's
health, he trying to quit
smoking, diet change, he
not being able to do
anything. She is pretty
stressed out herself.
It's going to be pretty rough
til he gets over the
withdrawal and gets to
feeling better.

11-8-99 - We worked on
projects at trailer today.
Not much goes on at
this park during the
week.

11-9-99 Max went fishing
and caught more fish.
He even got a 18"
Catfish.

I just worked on
paper work.

11-10-99 - Tried to make some sense out of insurance billings.

11-11-99 Max decided to try fishing challenge again. Not very good today. But he got 4. I continued my assault on insurance companies. Someday I might have it figured out.

Hope I get it done before the next thing happens.

11-12-99 Another beautiful day. It's time to move to Medina Lake. We will be staying there til after Christmas.

Got in early afternoon and got a favorite spot.

11-13-99 We've settled in here at Medina. It's such a much more progressive park than Columbus River was. We attended managers meeting this morn). Renewed acquaintance with some friends. This afternoon we did our Saturday sports watch on TV.

11-14-99 Out to breakfast and then for a nice long walk down the nature trail. Watched some Sunday sports and stayed put.

11-15-99 The big dentist day at Dr. Lelands at Lake Kiko TX. Max got evaluation on having his lower teeth capped and repaired. Oh! Wow! Good dentist but expensive. He was so happy with his upper teeth repair job 2 yrs ago. I just have to have 1 crown replaced. But all will be worth it in the end.

11-16-99 - Still having our nice weather.

We drove to Leon Valley today and checked out our route to the dentist office there. Did a little shopping and ate lunch out. We came back and rested and played a couple games of golf.

11-17-99 - We had hobo stew at club house today.

Played two games of miniature golf. Also took along walk.

Max washed truck. Now he feels better about that.

11-18-99 Max was off at 7:00 AM to get truck a tune up. I took an inventory of things in basement.

Also got a walk and did some cross stitch. He got home about 3:00 PM and was happy with the people working on truck.

We played miniature golf. I finally won a game. First time since we've been here

11-19-99 Took a drive to Bandera today. Then we drove another 13 mi. to Medina TX. Sure found out there was not much there. We came back and had lunch at a Chinese restaurant in Bandera.

Also got in a nap, 2 games miniature golf and a walk.

Made reservations into January for Del Rio & Big Bend National Park

11-20-99 Went to breakfast at Club house.

The rest of the day was our usual kind of Saturday watching football.

11-21-99 Laundry was the most work I did today

Gathered thoughts about going home for Christmas. Thoughts are running thru my head about purchasing a computer next summer.

Should we, shouldn't we.

11-22-99 - Max had dental appoint this afternoon. So we did our walk this morning.

While he was at dentist I worked on insurance papers.

His appointment was at 2:00 and he didn't get home til 5:00.

11-23-99 Still another nice sunny day.

I got my hair done and then we drove to Boerne Tx. Had lunch did a bit of looking around.

Max talked to a guy about transmissions. We were off to see if he could change our transmission

oil. He could. OK.
It was in same area as
a Walmart so I
went shopping there
while he stayed with
truck.

After all that we
went to groc store. It
was mad house. Just
2 days before Thanksgiving.
After groc shopping, we
stopped at Dairy Queen.
Yes I snitched. Probably
will pay for it tomorrow.
11-24-99 - This is Max's long
day at dentist. He had
to go to dentist office at Leon
Valley. His appointment was
at 10:00 A.M. He got home at
5:00. Long day for him.
But, the end results his
bottom teeth will be
much nicer.
I stayed home and
caught up on some paper
work and stuff.
Weather turned cooler. I
had to put jeans on. ☺

11-25-99 - Thanksgiving Day
Fixed deviled eggs &
a vegetable tray for
the big Thanksgiving
Dinner at Club house.
Watched traditional
parades. Talked to
Terry and family.
Went to dinner then
came back got watched
football and took nap.
I Gave Sue & family a
call and took a walk.
Max is doing good from
all the work he had
done on his teeth
yesterday.
11-26-99 - Picked up mail
and balanced check
book. Took a walk.
Not doing much these
days.
I need to finish Jeanette
cross stitch for Christmas.
Seems I'm getting a little
burned out of cross
stitch.
I must go on and finish it.

11-27-99 Another gorgeous day. We went to club house for breakfast.

We took a long walk today. We're doing it regularly now. Helps my diabetis and general health. Good for May too. I worked somemore on my cross stitch.

Took some pictures of Medina Lake today and the sunset.

11-28-99 - I decorated the trailer for Christmas today. Even put some lights in our little table this year.

Progressing with X stitch.

11-29-99. Dentist appointment this morn. Have to take old crown out and put temporary in. Have cavity under crown.

Everything went well. After all that we went to Bandera for lunch.

mouth is still numb but was able to eat. Now mouth feels like it was stretched and stamped on. I will survive.

I guess if Max can go thru all he has, I can make it with one tooth.

11-30-99 - Tues morn - Max just got started with washing trailer. I checked messages and Dr Leland (dentist) wanted him to call. We called. They wanted him to come to office. They had to do another impression. What we didn't know was they had to take the temporary crowns off and re-do all impressions. Well with having washed trailer and all that they were doing to him his blood pressure was up and also they were checking his pulse.

After 2 hours in chair, we were ready to come home. We stopped and got sandwiches and headed home. What a day.

12-1-99 - Max finished up trailer. He painted steps etc. I did windows.

12-2-99 Max waxed front of trailer. I went to laundry. We was really tired tonight.

12-3-99 - This is a no work day. Out to lunch and shopping at Boerne Tx. Even bought a few Christmas things.

12-4-99 - Truck died this morn. Alternator went out. Max was able to put battery charger on and get it started. He will go to garage on Mon. We stayed put at campground. Went to breakfast, played miniature golf, watched Ill basketball, went back to club house for supper. Stayed there for Christmas

auction. Came back &
watched some TV til mid-
night. Guess that was
enough for one day.
12-5-99 - With uncertainty
of truck, we stayed
put.
   Fixed some good old
beef and noodles
today.
   Made more progress with
my X-stitch. Got the ends
finished.
   May helped me get
the spacing right for
the sides.
   He's so good at that
kind of stuff.
12-6-99 - May was off early
to see about truck.
I stayed home and did
homework.
   When he got back truck
was O.K. All gauges
checked out good.
   Crazy truck.
   Meantime I did paper
work and then

did some preparation
for Christmas shopping
tomorrow. We're going
to ship this year.

12-7-99 Truck didn't start
this morning. Max put
charger on for awhile
It started.

We went to Sears in
San Antonio. They checked
battery that was OK.
So we did Christmas
shopping at Ingram Mall.
Came home and collapsed.

12-8-99 Stayed home today.
Truck didn't start this
morning.

Max called Ford garage
and got appoint for
Fri.

We went to lunch at
club house.

12-9-99 - Truck didn't
start again. Max put
charger charger on truck
last night. It started
right off. We were off
to continue our Christmas

shopping.

12-10-99 Max was off early for appointment with Ford Garage.

Wouldn't you know it, the truck started on its own this morn. To make a long story short. He went back to Tiller's and they put on a new alternator.

I stayed home and worked on projects.

He got home about 1:00. We played mini golf this P.M.

We're going to stay home tonight.

12-11-99 Something new this morn. We were getting rain. They haven't had rain since last June here.

We went to breakfast, signed up for extra time, worked on packing presents. I continued on cross stitch. Almost done. Going to make it after all.

12-12-99 Did laundry first thing today.

Next on agenda I worked on Christmas cards. My part is now done. Max has to seal them and put returns on. We can get them in mail.

This evening there was a spaghetti dinner at club house. We went and enjoyed.

12-13-99 - We went to Bandera Tx today to get all the presents shipped out. - A little more expensive this way but, a lot easier on us. Now when we get to Detroit we can just enjoy.

12-14-99 This morning I finished my cross stitch project for Jeanette. Happy! Happy Day.

This afternoon I washed it.

Now I need to do backing on it and press it.

Also had some book
work to do.
Then we played
miniature golf. Max
beat me by 1.
12-15-99 - Pressed the
cross stitch. It's done
ready to travel.
This afternoon we
went to Riverwalk in
San Antonio. It was our
Christmas out. It was
nice but weather was
cool and we ate
inside.
12-16-99 Got the shower
cleaned today.
This afternoon we flew
kites. We hadn't had a
kite in the air since
the festival.
Tonight I started a new
cross stitch.
No deadlines on this
one.
12-17-99 - Up early today.
I had an 8:30 hair
appoint. Then we

were off to Leon Valley for 10:00 final dentist appointment. I had 1 crown. But Max had 10. We were there for about 3 hours. Then we treated ourselves to lunch. Yes we could eat at Appleby's.

Came home got our walk in and stayed put.

12-18-99 Just took it easy today. Did a little X stitch and caught up on a few other things.

12-19-99 - Have been putting finishing touches on things. We leave 21st. Laundry is done, trailer cleaned.

Only have to do refrigerator yet and get packed.

12-20-99

Max ran an errand this morning and on way back he came thru gate and the

truck caught fire
under hood. Flames
were shooting out.
He and another man
got it out.
The fire was at the
alternator, we just
had replaced.
So he made call to
garage. They told him
to bring it in.
I stayed back and
proceeded to pack etc
so we could fly to
Novi tomorrow.
Meantime, at the garage
he was in drafts and
it was rainy & damp.
That didn't help the
cold he already had
started.
He got home about 4:30.
12-21-99. We got up at 4:15.
Chuck Reynolds from
here in park was going
to drive over truck
and take us to
airport.

in San Antonio. Everything was clicking into place. Plane was on time and we were on our way. First we flew to Houston and changed planes. Then it was on to St. Louis, Chicago and Detroit. Terry met us at 4:05 with sign in hand. It skid Robinson. With Luxury Limousine Service at bottom.

He took us to his house. Jeanette had a nice pot of chili waiting for us.

We ate that right away and we were off to watch Elle play indoor soccer.

Came back to the house and unpacked suit cases. Wow! What a day.

12-22-99 All settled in Detroit. Thankful we didn't have to go do

Christmas shopping.

12-23-99 - Now I'm starting with cold.

Sue and family are expected in around supper time.

They are coming from Chicago. Dadney had check up appointment this morning.

12-24-99 We have our family Christmas after breakfast a fun day.

Terry & family go to church at 4:00.

When they get back we have a nice Christmas dinner.

12-25-99 - Christmas Day. Terry & family have their Christmas. But, he is sick with flu and went back to bed for the day.

Jeanette & kids go to her mother's for awhile. Augie has been sick also.

12-26-99 - Iris doesn't feel well in morning. Coming down with flu. They leave about 4:00 PM. Things slow down a bit.

Max & I sneak in a nap.

12-27-99 - Things were slowed down a bit today.

12-28-99 This evening we went to watch Elle play another soccer game. Fun to watch these little girls.

12-29-99 - I washed, and Played some 50 with the kids again today.

12-30-99. I got clothes washed and we packed as we were flying out at 5:45.

Terry came and got us at 4:00. We got to airport. Plane was on time. Had a good flight back. But, shes 20 min

is a long flight.
Chuck and Alice met
us in San Antonio.
We were home by 11:30 PM.
12-31-99 - We watched some
football bowls today.
Went for a few groceries
before the new year.
This is the millenium.
There has been so much
hype about what would
happen as to how the
Computers would
survive changing to 00.
There is a party at
club house. We decided
not to go. We watched
New Years Eve's around
the world.
Just stayed in and
took care of our Colds.
Are we getting older
or what.
1-1-00. We watched
parades and more
football.
1-2-00 I'm beginning to
close out over Barkers

Jan 1999.

1-3-99:00 We went to Boerne Tx for groceries etc. Needed to fill refrigerator. It was pretty bare.

1-4-99:00 Still getting settled in from Christmas. Putting things away.

1-5-00 Went to club house for weekly stew lunch today.

1-6-00 Caught up on laundry We said our good-bys to Chuck & Alice & Ron & Lois. Had dinner at club house

1-7-00 - Moving day has arrived after nearly 2 months at Medina Lake. Now its on to American CC at Del Rio.

This is just a stop-over on our way to Big Bend Nat Pk. Also we like to go to Cripple Creek Steak House for their prime rib. Not the best thing for my diet. I consider it a special day.

1-8-00 - Weather turned very nice today. We did some shopping in Del Rio Tx.

Tonight we went to our favorite restaurant in this area. Cripple Creek Steak House. They have a superior prime rib.

1-9-00 Took it easy today. Watched some football.

1-10-00 We moved on to Alpine Tx, via Rte 90 About 200 mi. Towns were small, not very progressive. Lots of rock and also got into mountains. The Lost Alaskan is a nice park. We will be here 1 week.

1-11-00 Went to McDonald Observatory today at Ft Davis Tx.

They had big telescopes there. We sat in on part of a lecture. Both Max and I were totally lost as to what they were talking about. Anyway, the drive there was pretty & mountainous. Wes enjoyed that. We came back to Ft Davis and had lunch there.

1-12-00 This afternoon we drove to a gift shop in Alpine. We saw a 10 min movie about the Marfa Lights.

Then we drove to Marfa 20 miles away. Went in the old hotel that movie stars had stayed in while making the movie Giant. Such as Liz Taylor, Rock Hudson, James Dean.

Marfa is an old, old, Texas town.

We found a restaurant called Mike's Place to have dinner.

A Mexican restaurant. We decided to forgo Mexican food and had just

their cheeseburger.
Then we drove to area
where we could view
the Marfa Lights. They
had regular parking
area etc.
Now, these lights are
off in far, far distance.
They can't explain why
they are there. Many
scientist and other
people come to observe
them. They are totally
out in the middle of
nowhere. They move,
change, color, and who
knows what else.
1-13-00 Max went to wash
dirty truck.
I stayed put and
cleaned files.
1-14-00 Went to Davis St
Park today. Took a
drive thru.
The restaurant was
closed. We came back
to town of Ft Davis
and had lunch.

We came back and I worked some more on this very, very hard pretzel puzzle that Jon & Elle got me for my birthday.

1-15-00 - We flew kites today, here at campground. That got us a bit of exercise.

I gave up on the pretzel puzzle. Finding 2 pieces in an hour was no fun.

Now its back to cross stitch.

1-16-00 Just an easy day. Not much going on. Washed, watched some sports.

1-17-00 Moved south to Terlinga TX. In the mountains & desert. Very barren land. Very warm 80° today. We went to Terlingua Ghost Town.

Also visited an old

cemetary. They hardly
got the graves dug.
Very stony hard ground.
1-18-00 Went to a portion
of Big Bend National
Park today. Down Old
Maverick Road. A good
but dirt road. Through
the canyons, desert,
and mountains.
Unbelievable the scenery
and even a few people
lived out here once.
1-19-00 Today we took
the scenic route west
thru Lajitas and on
to Presidio.
Very scenic, the mountains,
desert, We toured an
old western movie set.
Near Presidio we even
saw farming along
the Rio Grande. Out of
the mountains and right
there it was level, and
land being irrigated.
Unbelievable after coming
thru such rugged

Country.

Oh yes the one "Big Hill" had a 15% grade. That's steep. But ole Ford made it.

1-20-00 We headed east into Big Bend State Park once again.

First we went to Basin area. Lots of green + trees there.

We headed on to Rio Grande Village into much more desert area. Then a little further and we were at Boquillas Mexico. This was far east corner of park.

When we stopped for lunch, I fell. We were walking to picnic area and I stepped in a deep whole. One skinned up knee, my glasses really bent. I landed on my shoulder and head. Well after

all that I'm just a little shaken up.
We headed home and took naps.
1-21-00 - Today we drove to Terlingua ghost town. There we had lunch at little restaurant called - When Pigs Fly Nothing fancy but nicely painted.
My bar-b-que sandwich was good. Max's chicken was over cooked.
1-22-00 We stayed put today. I caught up on my picture album. At least I'm caught up til we get 3 more rolls of film developed.
1-23-00 This was a stay put day. Watched the football playoffs.
1-24-00 Moved on north to Pecos TX to Trapark (a SKP). This will be just a stopover for 2 days.

1-25-00 Went shopping - well made a stop at Walmart + grocery. Only shopping for necessities.

Went to pizza hut for lunch.

1-26-00 Moved on to Lakewood N Mex. This park is north of Carlsbad N.M. We've been here before. Really live in desert here. I'm not feeling to good. Like a cold but I think its allergies.

1-27-00 I stayed in today. That wind is out of north. It's only about 50°.

Max went to social hour. The people probably think he has no wife. Better watch out for the widows.

1-28-00 We've had a cold spell come in. It only was up to 42° today.

made a pot of chili and stayed put.

1-29-00 - Still cold here. Tonight we went to club house for hobo stew.

1-30-00 A little bit warmer today. We did our walk. Had our insulated jackets on. Going into wind, it's still very cold. Its super bowl Sunday. I've taken Tennessee. My betting buddy Jerry has LA Rams.

Well, I goofed this year and picked the wrong team. His team won 23-16. I probably have a message tomorrow.

1-31-00 Got a ton of mail today so I spent most of my day working on it.

2-1-00 We had 10 min worth of snow flurries in the desert here today ugh!

This evening we went across street to Lenny & Bev Ratzlaffs' They are from South Dakota. He is the man that got Max into kiting.

2-2-00 We had ~~fog~~ sunshine at 7:45 A.M. Fog rolled in at 8:00 A.M. This afternoon it warmed up and we took our jackets off. Went into Walmart and then met group at Pizza Inn for Pizza. Nice social time with these people.

2-3-00 - The weather warmed up today. - 70°
Max got ~~truck~~ brakes adjusted & cleaned truck
I just did this & that and whatever. I did finish my Hummel Cross stitch. Just have to wash it now.

2-4-00 I started my X-stitch project for the Berkey Robinson reunion.

Max flew kites with
Lenny.

2-5-00 Sunny & windy &
still fairly cold.
I'll be glad when we
move on.
We went to pancake
breakfast at club
house today. $3 for
both of us. Can't beat
it.
I worked on picture
book and new cross
stitch.
Max painted hitch
& steps.

2-6-00 Finally a warm &
sunny day.
We went to Carlsbad
had Sunday dinner
there.
Went to local park
along the Pecos River
and took a walk.
Need more days like
this.

2-7-00 Weather continuing
to warm up daytime.

Max is getting his
outside work done.
I'm cleaning inside.
Hopefully we will move
on ~~Sunday~~ Monday and
start playing again.

2-8-00 Max continued work
on roof.
I walked to post office
and took care of mails.

2-9-00 Finally got my hair
cut & set today. Enjoyed
a nice dinner out at
K-Bobs Restaurant and
got 2 very nice Carnations
for Valentines Day. It's
early but that's OK.

2-10-00 I helped Max wash
trailer today. We worked
together He wiped top ½ &
I did bottom ½. And we
rested along the way.
When he does it alone,
he works so hard and
hardly rests.

I think I have a
permanet job now but
that's O.K

2-11-00 The wind was very strong again today. Temp. was in 70's. I worked on taxes today. I did the rough figuring. Looks like we get back what I expected. That will be a good amount toward the computer.

2-12-00 The Ranch had their Valentine Dinner tonight. They furnished the main course. Ham, chicken & baked beans. That is a little different. The people took salads & desserts.

Max and I also helped clean up afterwards. We've enjoyed their activities & friendship. It was the least we could do.

The wind was really bad all day again

2-13-00 Wind more calm today. don't think

this park is really the place for us to settle down

2-14-00 Moved on today through some good mountains. Very scenic drive. We stopped in Cloudcroft NM for lunch. We had the daily special. Lunch cost us $10.39. That was for both of us. I'm a cheap Valentine Date. We drove on to the Dream Catcher Park at Deming NM. Another SKP park.

They were having a spaghetti dinner there. We joined in. Spaghetti bread, salad, drink + desert $3.50 each.

The dinner Sat night cost us $5. This noon $10 and tonight $7.00. Valentine meals total $22.00 for 2. Are we economizing or what.

2-15-00 A sunny day. Went to town and made a few purchases of necessities. Did a little work at trailer. Enjoyed the view of the mountains around us.

2-16-00 drove out of Deming today to a Back Way Road. This took us into mountains. Drove thru Hillsboro & Kingston. Went on thru Emery Pass in the Gila National Forest. Very scenic drive. Even saw snow on side of mountains.

Also realized we had taken this same drive in 47. Parts we remembered and parts we didn't.

Needed some lunch. Finally came to a gas stop that had Subways.

After lunch we

wound our way
back to Deming.

2-17-00 Very windy today.
Did laundry, groceries.
Even made it to dinner
with a group at the
park. The restaurant was
K-Bob's. We were at a
K Bobs in Artesia NM.
Not fancy but good.

2-18-00 Headed our rig
west today toward
Benson Az. No wind.
Thank goodness.
Going to stay at Pato Blanco
Lakes RV park.
Went to post office. No
mail yet. Its closed Sat.
No mail on Mon — Pres
Day. So we will stay
over til Tues.

2-19-00 Drove to Tombstone AZ
We've been here before.
Its a neat little town to
come to. They stage
shout outs in broad day
light.
Had lunch at the

Longhorn on the corner.

2-20-00 Today is Daytona 500. Father wants to see it from start to finish. So we are staying put today.

2-21-00
We went to Chinese restaurant today. Then father found a place for hair cut. Supposedly she was closed on Monday but she did cut his hair.

2-22-00 Moving day once again. But 1st Max had to go to Post Office to pick up our mail. Couldn't get it tel 9:30. Max going to Post Office is another story. Anyway we moved on to Hickiwan Trails RV Resort near Ajo Az. This is a nice campground in the desert. It is a campground in conjunction with Indian Casino. We got in and set up and no one around to take our money. Found out from people around us. If they show up to take money pay them. If not you've had free camping. So we accepted that and settled in.

2-23-00 Got around and took a walk in the desert.

Their are several different kinds of Cactus here. Actually took a good long walk. Only live animals we saw, was a few lizards. and a few birds.

2-24-00 We explored the town of Ajo AZ today. We live in the real desert. But, the plaza in town had grass

so beautiful green.
At one time there was
a copper mine in
this town. Now its
shut down.
At that time it
was a thriving
community.
2-25-00 We drove to
Organ Pipe National
Monument Park today
Its near the border
of Mexico.
Its more of the varieties
of cactus.
Actually we are learning
the different names
of cactus.
While I eating dinner
tonight, we watched
a couple coyotes
come along edge of
park.
2-26-00 We explored the
desert today.
With camera in hand
we took off for a
hike in the desert

I took pictures of all different kinds of cactus. Almost used a whole roll of film. Can't wait to see how they turned out.

We got back in time to watch I.U. upset Mich State. Good game. After that I worked on picture book. Got Christmas pictures caught up.

2-27-00 Just a stay home day today.

2-28-00 Moved on to Columbia River Adv. at Yuma Az. Didn't have reservation but could get a spot and stay 3 nights on our RPI Card.

After setting up we went to Imperial Dam to check out a park there. It was 20 miles out, Crowded, dirty & lots of dust from Construction going on.

Came back to Yuma
and found a Good
Sam park we liked.
Will move there Thurs.
2-29-00 - Scouted Yuma
today. Couldn't remember
about this town. But
places began to come
back to us as we
drove around.
Had our lunch at
Appleby's. Used our
gift certificate from
Christmas and the Boeks.
3-1-00 We checked out
this park today. Even
got laundry done
3-2-00 Our 3 nights were
up today. We moved to
a new park Las Quintas
Oasis for 4 days.
We kidded about not
being tired. It was
less than 10 miles
away.
We went to a Sedlotsky's
for lunch. But, had
to wait to get in

They had, had a robbery. And still dusting for finger prints.
They finished and we had lunch.
Looked at carpeting in new RVs after lunch.
We were checking out their carpets.
We would like to get new carpeting when we got back to Indiana.

3-3-00 Post office trip & lunch. That was OK.
Then bought new coffee pot. Tired of messing with old one.
Then supposedly we were looking for trailer carpet but got interested in a new Newmar Travel Trailer. It was nice. No we didn't buy it. Came home!

3-4-00 - Our Saturday stay home day. Took care of mail etc. Watched some spots.

It thundered & lightning and even got some rain this evening.

3-5-00 I mentioned going out for breakfast and Max was up out of chair in a flash. He shaved and got dressed right now.

The weather turned cold and nasty.

We stayed put the rest of the day.

3-6-00 Moving day once again to Pio Pico near San Diego.

We had to take a spot on one side of road for 24 hrs.

Tomorrow we'll get a permanet spot.

3-7-00 - By 11:30 AM we were able to move across road to full hook up site.

It rained off and on most of the day.

This evening we called Deb Troyer. We will go see them on Sunday.

3-9-00 A day in Tiajuna Mex. We took a bus tour from the camp-ground at 8:15 AM. Lady bus driver of Mexican decent. Lived in Mexico & San Diego. New area well very knowledgeable about it.

We opted for a tour of Tijuana away from shopping district for first hour. She took us up & down those narrow streets with that big bus. Put some of those RV drivers to shame.

4 million people live in Tiajuna.

Then we came back to the shopping area. I got to haggle over several items) with merchant.

I bought earrings for $10. He first wanted $18. Then I picked out bracelet for $157. After telling him no many times I got it for $20.

On to next store - I bought sun catcher for $7. He wanted 14.50.

Then I encountered man on street with lots of necklaces on his arm. Finally, I ended up with just 1 for $5.00. Did I need these things no. But, I had fun dealing with them.

Then we had lunch in Mexican restaurant with a couple from Washington State.

After lunch we headed for San Diego.

Stopped at Coronado Hotel and Old Towne.

A fun, good, interesting

day. The tour part
only cost us $38 for
both. Can't beat that
with an excellent tour
guide.

3-10-00 - Max's back is
really hurting him. So
we just stayed home
today. Except for a run
to Post Office.

We watched the Big Ten
tourney. 3 of 4 teams were
upset today.

3-11-00 Max's back still giving
him real fits.
So much basket ball. We
were tired of it.
I worked on picture
book. Have lots of
pictures to catch up.
Having nice sunny
weather and that's
helpful.

3-12-00 Forgot to get milk
yesterday. That's an excuse
to go to club house for
breakfast.
They had craft show

on patio. Found several
things there we couldn't
live without.
Came back to trailer
Got around and drove
a fast pace on California
freeways to Deb & Dave
Troyers.
Visited a while and
went to lunch at a
place called Soup
Plantation. What a
salad bar!
Came back to their
house and visited
a little more. Took that
fast pace drive home.
3-13-00 - I got around to
go get newspaper this
morning so we would
have brackets for NCAA
tourney.
Had trouble with money
and machine. Got
wet from sprinklers on
way back. Had to go
back to get 2nd paper.
Oh well, I made it.

Next thing was to do some phoning and making reservations. Frustration with phones. not getting thru etc. Then had message from Sue. She had bad cold, Called her and tried to give her a shoulder to lean on. Its hard when you're away.

Finally got lunch and took a nap.

3-14-00 This day was better than yesterday. Got phoning completed, laundry done, found out Sue was doing much better and took a long walk. Good day.

3-15-00 We drove to Silver Strand Beach on the Pacific today.

Took a walk on the beach. Came back to truck and had lunch.

We rested a bit and then went kite flying

The sun was out part of the time. But that breeze was pretty chilly. We didn't take jackets but we endured.

I went prepared to take my top shirt off and get a sun tan.

Stopped at grocery store, came back home and collapsed. Fun Day!

3-16-00 Marilyn arrived with Deb around 10:30. So good to see her again. Deb had to go back to work.

Marilyn settled in and came over for afternoon. We talked & talked.

We took a break and she came over for supper with us. Max cooked steaks on grill.

We all watched NCAA tournament and she

went back to her
trailer for the night.
3-17-00 - We took Marilyn
to Jamacha Junction
for lunch. Had lunch
at Appleby's.
Then she & I did
some shopping. Fun
to have a woman to
shop with.
We came back and
watched more NCAA's.
3-18-00 Today we started
out with breakfast at
club house. Then we
took in flea market
at campground.
Next we all went to
Olympic Training Ctr and
had a tour there.
Came back, relaxed,
watched more NCAA.
The Troyer family arrived
around 3:00 P.M.
Visited with them.
We came back & max &
I had supper and
collapsed watching a

movie for evening.

3-19-00 - We said our good-byes to Marilyn and the Trogen family about 5:00 PM.

Got things around to move tomorrow.

3-20-00 - This was a traveling day. The weather started with a little sprinkle but sun came thru. After 1 1/2 hours of good travel up Hwy 15, the wind picked up. It was really blowing. Really had to pay attention. Wind gusts were 40 mPH plus.

We took care and reached our destination about 2:00 PM.

Our campground is an Oasis in desert. We got set up and stayed put rest of the day. The winds blew even harder.

Sure glad we are off the road.

3-21-00 We stayed put today. Still had some wind.

I worked on several projects.

I always have something to do. Don't understand how people get bored.

3-22-00 We moved another 200 miles today to Beatty NV. Saw lots more mountains and desert.

The winds of time and the hot desert sun has put interesting scenery in those mountains.

3-23-00 We went to Scotty's Castle today.

This castle was built in death valley around 1922. There is nothing but mountains & desert around it for miles. It was very modern for its time.

Also went to Ubehebe Crater. This crater was formed from a volcano. I forgot to mention Jack that took us on tour of castle. He talked as if he was living the time the castle was built.

3-24-00 Filled the gas tank and took off for Death Valley National Park. This is another unbelievable area. There is 3.3 million acres here. The mountains have so many minerals in them. The coloring is spectacular. Our first stop was Death Valley Ranch. We ate lunch there. You can vacation here. They have a hotel, golf course horse back riding - all kinds of things to do. An Oasis in the desert. We drove on to an area called

Bad Water. At this point you are 298' below sea level.

We walked the salt path aways out.

This area used to be a lake.

The salt taste is even saltier than the ocean.

At this point we turned around and headed home.

A really spectacular day.

I almost forgot at a ghost town just out of Beatty we stopped and looked around. Its called ~~Beatty~~ Rhyolite. There was a house there made from bottles. Many beer bottles. They found gold in these hills & mountains. It was once a thriving area.

3-25-00

Today was catch up day. Took care of mail, jest rested and watched the NCAA tournament.

3-26-00 Another beautiful day. We walked to restaurant for breakfast and then stayed put the rest of day.

I did laundry and we watched some more basketball.

3-27-00 Staying put here at Beatty, NV.

I'm catching up on some projects.

I now have my picture book up to date. Just 1 thing wrong I have 2 more rolls to be developed. Also my picture book is almost full. This is second book since last May 99. We've really been seeing some neat things this year.

3-28-00 Continued working on projects today.

3-29-00 This was moving day to Las Vegas NM. We're staying at Silverton RV Park.

We took care of getting hair appointment for me. Max got his hair cut. Went to Walmart and got some pictures developed. Now I have more to do in picture book. Didn't gamble any money yet.

3-30-00 We went to Silverton Casino for lunch today. After lunch we tried our hand at poker machines. Max broke even but I came away with a hole in my pocket. As any good gambler would say. I'll get it back next time.

3-31-00 This was stay

home and take care
of business day.
I finished Indiana State
taxes.

4-1-00 - Finally, my perm
day arrived. 9:00 I'm
at beauty shop.
I was desperate. - Perm
went well and I was am
happy.
Stopped for lunch on
way home.
Watched NCAA today.

4-2-00 Went to Champagne
Brunch at Silverton
then we took shuttle
to downtown strip
Walked a little seeing
the sites, and gambled
a little. Also lost
a bit. But the machines
were better to me than
time before.

4-3-00 - We stayed
home today.
Ray installed new
brake control. I balanced
books for mo & quarter

We watched final game of NCAA tournament. Mich State won. Jeanette won the pool.

That's 2 for her this year. Football + basketball.

4-4-00 We shopped for Sue's birthday present. Then lunch at our favorite place Schlotskys. We next went gambling at Jokers Wild on Boulder Hwy.

Would you believe I actually came out with more money than I went in with.

I had a fun afternoon. This evening we went to Fremont Street downtown. We saw the light display 2 times. Each one is different.

4-5-00 We went to Las Vegas Motor Speedway today.

Quite a big racing

complex.

We did see a couple cars doing practice laps. Also the drag-sters were getting ready for races this weekend.

4-6-00 - Today we took in the show we had comp-limentary passes to. It was at Stratosphere. Show was 1 hour. A variety show. Not very good!

We came back & ate at Silverton & gambled a little there. That was not good either.

4-7-00 Drove to Hoover Dam today. It how The area has sure changed since we were there in 87. They've commercial-ized it. Even have a parking garage there. Also they've built a casino on the way. We came back to Henderson and ate supper.

We tried gambling at the spot we did the other day — Jokers Wild. I won some money that day. The Old Joker took it all today.

4-8-00 Its our 44th Anniversary. We had dinner at a very nice Chinese Restaurant at New York-New York complex here in Vegas. We had an exceptional waiter. Very good food.

Then we went to Broadway Theater and saw Lord of the Dance. It's an Irish Dance Group. One fabulous show!

Very nice anniv.!

4-9-00 Can't play everyday. Did laundry today.

4-10-00 - Took another shot at the slot machines today.

They've just not treated us very good this time. I finally played the nickle slots and played quite awhile on my $1.

Finally said to heck with it and came home.

4-11-00 Got things around for our move tomorrow. We went to Casino and gambled one last time. Max wore his lucky hat and won 160-254 I don't know why he didn't do that before.

4-12-00 Beautiful day to travel. We took Route 93 out of Las Vegas to Hoover Dam. Very mountainous, Then we traveled on south. Up & over & down the mountains Very rocky terrain. to Kingman Az. There we picked up Rte 40 and headed east to Williams Az.

4-13-00 We explored Route 66 shops in Williams today. Route 66 used to be the main road west in the 40's & 50's. We took Rte 66 in 1957 when we came west on vacation. At that time you paid $6-$7 per night for motel room.

4-14-00 Moved to a TT park - Verde Valley at Cottonwood AZ A real nice park. Never stayed here before.

4-15-00 Picked up mail and came back and stayed put.

This evening there was entertainment at club house. A guy & his wife performed. A 2 hr show. Very good.

4-16-00 Today is Sue's birthday. She is 42 today. Can't believe it.

Gave her a call this
evening.
4-17-00 We went to a
computer class.
Jerry Grosman was
excellent. Even though
we only sat in on
one of his classes.
We learned alot.
4-18-00 Max went to
get tires rotated +
balanced. Came back
said they would have
4 new tires ready for
us tomorrow. Ouch!
But we need good tires.
This PM we drove to
Clarkdale AZ and went
to TUZIGOOT National
Monument. The Sinagua
Indians lived here at
one time. But no one
knows what happened
to them. They just
disappeared.
4-19-00 We went to
Blazing M Ranch in
Cottonwood to a

chuck wagon dinner.
Plus they had enter-
tainment after dinner.
Fun time I enjoyed.
4-20-00 Our on the go
days contenue. We
took Verde Valley Train
to Perkinsville today.
One beautiful trip
thru the canyons.
We chugged along
about 10 miles an
hour. It was a 40 mile
round trip. Lots of
untouched nature.
4-21-00 Day started out
cloudy but we had
hopes for sun to come
out it did.
We took one beautiful
drive up 89 A to Sedona
and on to Oak Creek
Canyon.
Found a real nice
place to go to lunch
called Spices. Very neatly
decorated.
Came home, rested awhile

and went to entertain-
ment here at park.
A husband-wife duo.
Called Dump Station
Review. Very good.
4-22-00 A work day-Today
Max & I washed the
trailer. It looks good,
but, my aching body.
We took showers and
went to the Easter
Dinner here at park.
It was Easter eve but
that's when this park
had their Easter Dinner
Came home and collapsed
in chair.
Went to bed at 10:00.
Both Max & I got up.
We were too tired to
sleep.
He read and I straight-
end out a mess
in my cross stitch.
4-23-00 A very quiet
Easter Sunday.
We stayed put and
recuperated from

washing trailer.

4-24-00 - This is wash truck day.

We rewarded ourselves by going to dinner in Cottonwood.

4-25-00 Just did laundry today and stayed put.

4-26-00 Moved on to Thoreau N.M.

The drive out of Verde Valley was a long hard pull. But old Ford made it. We then took Rte 40 at Flagstaff AZ to Thoreau. The trucks were many on this route. But Max paid attention and we made it O.K.

4-27-00 - Really not much going on in town of Thoreau.

Strictly Indian Reservation.

We did eat at Wagon Wheel Restaurant. This

was an O.K. place.

4-28-00 We moved on north of Albuquerque today to a Corps of Engineers Park called Jetilla Peak Reck Area. Very scenic, secluded place. Getting here we went from 1 Indian Reservation to another.

It will be fine for 3 days.

4-29-00 - Quite a wind we had yesterday. Just about lost our awning.

We took a nice hike down side of hill toward lake. Easy going down but got the heart pumping coming up.

Watched NBA basketball rest of day.

4-30-00

Sun was cooler again and had some

wind. We stayed
put.

5-1-00 Today, we headed
for Trinidad Co.
Much better weather.
A couple mountain
passes were real
good ones. but we
made them O.K.

5-2-00 Spent the day
re-grouping, groceries -
Walmart etc.

5-3-00 Headed for Colo Spgs
Co. today Beautiful day.
We arrived at Fountain
Creek CG shortly before
noon. It is an OK CG.
Very crowded. But, we
will be on the go
quite a bit, so it
will be OK.

5-4-00 We got reservation
to go to top of Pike's Peak
on Cog Railway today. We
did this in 1969. Only
remembered parts of the
trip.
Weather is being very

cooperative. Just a
pretty, warm 80° spring
day.
5-5-00 - We picked up
mail today.
Then we had lunch
on a patio of a pub
and went to tour
Miramount Castle.
It had 46 rooms and
was on 4 floors.
Came home and
took a nap.
5-6-00 We went to
Current Outlet today.
This is a company I've
bought ✗ wrapping
paper, cards, etc for
years by catalog.
Well, most of what I
got was for Sue &
grand-kids. I had fun
shopping.
Next we went downtown
to Antlers Mark Hotel.
This used to be just
the Antlers hotel.
They have remodeled

it so, I couldn't tell there was any part of it left.

I stayed here in 50's when Carole Keebel and I came here on vacation.

We had lunch at the microbrewery in the hotel.

5-7-00 - This was a day to stay home & do nothing.

5-8-00 The rains finally caught up with us. We haven't seen rain of any quantity since last Dec. The day before we flew home for Christmas it rained at Medina Lake. But anyway, we went to Van Briggle Pottery this afternoon.

Found out the lamp we gave Sue was no longer made.

If I send them a picture they will

authencitate it.
We bought this lamp
in 62-64.
Made a stop next
at Hobby Lobby.
Also went to a Shoe
store. My point is
I didn't spend any
money.
Nothing just hit me.
5-9-00 - This was a
busy day. Did laundry
then after lunch we
went to Garden of Gods
Park. So pretty in the
red rock. We took hike
of about 1 mile.
May wasn't really
feeling good. I think the
altitude was affecting
him. We made it back
to truck and rested.
Then we came on home.
5-10-00 We drove to
Royal Gorge today. That's
about an hour from
Colo Spgs.
We took Rte 115. Its

a very scenic drive.

Of course, the things at Royal Gorge have changed in 35 yrs. We rode the incline, walked across the bridge, had lunch on other side.

Then we took the 7 min. train ride on a miniature train around the park. Max was getting such a kick out of it.

5-11-00 We drove to U S Air Force Academy today. We've been here before. Back in 69 or 70 I think. Just like everything else, its grown.

What an excellent complex to train our young men & women.

5-12-00 What a day. First I got hair cut, & set.

I think the beautician

might have been gay.
But, he was good.
Next we went to Olympic
Training Center got a
tour there. Also saw
several demonstrations
by athletes. Men's
gymnastics, Men's wheel
chair rugby, and ladies
volley ball.
We grabbed a bite
of lunch, and rested
then at 5:30 we had
dinner at Juniper Valley
Ranch. We went out
Rte 115 west of Colo Springs.
This was at a very
unique old ranch house.
We took some pictures.
Stone floor, very quaint
adobe house.
We had chicken as
our main Course.
First my appetizer was
cherry cider. May had
curry consume soup.
We had biscuits, apple
butter, cold slaw,

riced potatoes. Okkra
Casserole + gravy.
For dessert we had
Mexican Custard - Entia
Yemmmmmy! Coffee +
ice tea.

We found out about
this place in Country
Discoveries magazine.
Also talked with owner
+ waitress. Very pleasant
evening.

5-13-00 Taking it easy
today. Did go to post office
+ grocery.

Started on picture book.
I have lots of pictures to
put in again.

5-14-00 - It was Mother's Day
today.

We stayed put. Just
didn't want to fight crowds
at restaurants. We had our
special dinner on Fri night.
We talked to Jerry on Sat
night and Sue this
evening. So all that added
up to a special Mother's Day.

5-15-00 - Thinking ahead to some dress up times in Elkhart I decided it was time for a little shopping. Some shoes & slacks took care of that.

We had lunch at mall finished shopping and came home.

5-16-00 Stayed put today. Got ready for move tomorrow.

5-17-00 Day started out nice. We drove to Stratton Co, not far from eastern border of Co. When we arrived wind started picking up. It was blowing harder as Max was setting up.

As the afternoon progressed, so did the wind.

We had gusts to 70 MPH. Now!

Lost our slide out.

awening. It ripped
loose And Max went
out and cut it off.
Sitting in the slideout.
The vibrations would
lift my chair.
And the winds continued
all night.
We checked the weather
station and Max checked
things outside.
Never have we been
in such a wind.
5-18-00. Still some wind
today. Not bad though.
Also getting a little rain
and colder.
This afternoon it got
better.
We went over to antique
car museum and craft
store.
5-19-00 Got up to nice
sunshine and headed
east for Salina Ks via
Interstate 70.
This was a long way
to go. Almost 300 mi.

Things went well.
First, we stopped at
a Good Sam Park on
west side of Salina.
We didn't like that
so we came on to
a KOA.

We usualy don't pick
KOAs but at least it
was level.

Will stay here for
the week-end.

5-20-00 - This was a
normal Saturday. We
did a little shopping
and watched some
sports.

5-21-00 We walked down
the road to Denny's
Restaurant for breakfast.
Came back & watched
Indy Time Trials &
basketball.

5-22-00 Moved on via
Rte 70 today to Bonner
Springs Ks.
Nothing much at this
park, but, OK for

2 nights.

5-23-00 We did some exploring around the area today.

Drove to Leavenworth for lunch.

When we got home I worked more on Pictures. Slowly getting caught up.

5-24-00 Another day on the move. Kansas City was no problem.

It was interstate 70 that was rough.

We soon found a road north to 24 and took that to Hannibal Mo. We stopped at Injun Joe CG.

It was hot, but, we parked under nice trees and had grass for a change.

5-25-00 It is May's birthday. He picked what we would do today.

We explored Hannibal

Mo.
It included a Mark
Twain Museum tour.
A tour of a 30 room
mansion and just
seeing the sight of
Hannibal.
Mark Twain's boyhood
home also.
Our trolley tour of the
area, was one of the
worst tours we've
ever been on.
From the driver to
the guide to the streets
to the trolley itself - BAD!
5-26-00 Moving day again.
This was a major move
7 hrs on the road.
Started out in rain
and had light rain off
and on all day.
Upon on arrival at
White Oaks on the Lake
campground at Monticello,
In, we checked in
and the spot we had
was next to the

woods. Over door would have been opening up in the road.

So, we went back to office and they gave us a very nice civilized spot.

You don't put a 33' TT on 2 tent sites.

Everything is well, now and we are set for the week-end.

Suppose to rain, so we will take one day at a time.

5-27-00 Not much going on. It's a drizzly day. I worked on picture album.

5-28-00 Max got biscuits and gravy at little cafe at campground. They didn't have anything else for breakfast.

He brought it back and I fixed my own breakfast. We were set to watch the

Indy 500 today.
Well they had a 3hr rain
delay. But, they did
get race run.
I slept thru part of
it.
Just a rainy sleepy day.
5-30-00 Sunshine finally.
Did some cleaning &
went to town to laundry
Found an exceptionally
nice laundry.
Got lunch at McDonald's
and came home.
Got things around to
move back to Elkhart.
I'm really ready.
5-30-00
Upon arrival in Elkhart/
Goshen we couldn't get
on to our spot.
So we took temporary
spot.
New managers and
things are different.
5-30-00. Went to Sue's
after school. And had
supper with them.
So glad to see them

5-31-00 We took it easy today.

I slept during the rains.

This evening we went to Danny's 6th grade graduation. We're so proud of him.

6-1-00 Did some shopping & business this morn. This afternoon we went to Oxbow school and watched the staff play softball against the 6th grade students. Went for groceries afterward and came home and stayed put. No

6-2-00 we didn't stay put. I went to Sue's over-night. They had meeting early next morn and Sue had to work all day.

6-2-00. Now I'm at Sue's with Danny & Iris. Iris helped me with computer and then we played a new game in afternoon.

This evening we ate at Bob Evans & came home and collapsed.

6-3-00 They finally got electric straightened out here at campground. We moved to our regular spot around noon.

We just stayed put the rest of the day.

6-4-00 We helped Danny celebrate his 13th birthday today. Had cake + ice cream with him.

6-5-00 Rainy this morning.

Got my eyes tested this morning. No cataracts, glacoma, no problems for diabetes. Getting new glasses and some change to presc. That was all good news. Went to Sue's. Cancelled trip to cemetary.

She then helped me

with finding info about Dell Computer on internet. Ended up I called and ordered one. I'm ready for it. Also excited.

I'm now thinking what all I will put on it. Next I have to find a printer.

Came home and collapsed after all that brain work.

6-6-00 We went to Sue's and then on to cemetery to do our annual clean up at the graves.

We all stopped at Wendy's for lunch.

6-7-00 Stayed put today. Did some re-arranging and worked on picture book.

8-00 Today was stay home day and work some more on picture albums. We did go to River Inn in Bristol and then took a drive to Middlebury.

6-9-00 — This started just as a normal day. At 1:00 we went to Sue's to stay with kids. Things were going well til Air Express arrived with computer. I immediately started unpacking computer. I was trying to wash clothes, work on computer. Kids were taking care of themselves.

We came home around 4:00.

Max took care of the manager's dogs. Three of them. They're yappers and hard to catch. We got them outside finally.

Next we went for some computer supplies. Finally decided to pick up subway sandwiches and came home.

At least I can turn on computer and get in and out of it. Watched a basketball game and went to bed. Whew! what a day.

6-10-00 A slower day today. Spent quite a bit of time getting acquainted with computer.

It's a very slow process for me.

6-11-00 We moved to Sue's this PM.

We have to move everything out of trailer for new carpet. Iris was our helper.

6-12-00 Max took Trailer to All Brand RV for carpet.

I stayed at Sue's and washed bedding and clothes.

6-13-00 Trailer was done at 10:30.

We picked up trailer.

Carpet looked real
nice.
We came back to Sue's
~~order~~ put everything
back in trailer.
We are tired with
every part of our body
hurting.
It's very nice. I like
it. It was worth it.
6-14-00 This morning we
moved back to Twin
Pines. Now we are
settled until reunion.
It started raining again
this PM. We just stayed
put.
6-15-00 We took truck to
get starter worked on.
I worked on computer.
Progressing a little with
that.
We went with Bock
family to MDA camp to
see Danny.
Sixty two campers there.
All with some form of MD

6-16-00 We stocked up on groceries today. Both got hair cuts this P.m. Went to Office Max store to try and decide on computer. No decision yet. More homework to do.

6-17-00 Iris stayed with us til 1:00. Sue & Jim had to pick up Danny. We worked on her picture album.

Also she beat me in Yatzee. 5 games.

After she left we hung draperies. They are freshly cleaned from cleaners.

The rest of our day we watched the US open golf tournament.

6-18-00 We are up bright and early this morn. At 7:40 we are heading to the clinic for our blood work. Our physical is tomorrow.

After clinic we went to breakfast at Bob Evans.

Next stop at a computer store. We checked out printer and scanner. Didn't buy today.

We did check out a small table in Goshen, to put beside chair. Got that. It folds. That helps us keep things at a minimum as far as adding things to trailer.

Came home. Max took truck back to garage. Starter not working good. Gone for 2 hours.

This evening we worked with GTE to get voice mail activated. Finally got that accomplished.

What a day!

Watched the Pacers & Lakers play basketball tonight. Pacers got beat! 😠

Tired, went to bed.

6-20-00 - Today is physical day. Dr was very pleased with my control of sugar and my health in general. Max got a thumbs up report also.

We drove to Michaels in Mishawaka and got new mat for family picture frame. Then we splurged and went to Olive Garden for dinner.

I came home very tired and slept most of evening.

6-21-00 Stayed put today. We got some jobs done at trailer.

I ~~got~~ polished the woodwork in the living dining area.

6-22-00 May took me to Marilyns this morning. We met her 3 dogs, Whew! I couldn't handle 3 dogs. 1 Yes - 3 No.

We left and Marilyn and I went shopping. First we had a nice lunch at Great Wall, then to Mishawaka. Just got a few things here and there.

Ended our day about 4:00PM.

A nice day out with a friend.

6-23-00 - Started out the day at the computer store with getting printer & scanner. & having computer class.

After lunch it was off to laundry.

Just finding a lot to keep us busy.

6-24-00 - Off to breakfast this morn at Bulldog Saloon to have breakfast with class of 1950. About 30 people attend. It's fun.

Came home and stayed put rest of day. I

worked on computer.

6-25-00 Did some more work on computer today. Also hooked up printer and scanner. Everything is still a challenge right now. We did go to Mill Race Trail in Goshen and took a nice long walk.

6-26-00 Oops my hot fudge sundae that I had yesterday really took its toll on my sugar this morn.

I must be better today! I went to Sue's this afternoon.

She & Danny gave me some help with my computer.

6-27-00 We were up and gone early.

I dropped Max off at Sues. He helped her get things to dump.

I went on to get a perm.

We then got a ton of groceries. Well not really.

But, the refrigerator was very low.

Stayed home rest of the day and worked on computer.

6-28-00 – This afternoon we visited Max's sister Lola. At 92, she is doing good, but age is beginning to catch up with her.

She still has her sense of humor.

We enjoyed a few good laughs with her.

6-29-00 Finished the wood cleaning in bath & bedrooms today. This ~~morning~~ evening was our annual dinner out with Newburgs and Kiefers at Heinies Restaurant. A good time was had by all.

6-30-00 This was a day to take care of things at home.

Caught up picture books once again.

It is an on-going work in progress of working on computer.

7-1-00 Balanced the books today. Both on computer and manually. Real accomplishment. Stayed put all day.

7-2-00 Max & I went to breakfast at Mayberry Cafe. Then we took a drive up to Baldwin Lake. We saw several people at Hollywood Shores that we camped with there.

7-3-00 Finished my inside trailer cleaning. Vents & shower. Now I've been over everything.

I can help Max outside.

7-4-00 Iris came and went swimming with

us this afternoon.
Then we all went to
her house for a
campfire supper.
Puggy pies & some mores.
Gooooood.
Then it was off to
the fireworks.
We sat on the upper
level of the parking
garage downtown.
A good 4th of July.
7-5-00 Today was the
start of our volunteer
work for MDA.
We help Sue every
year with mailing
for abate ride.
We do this at her
house. We work 10:00 —
4:00.
Also got washing done
while there.
We were 2 pooped
puppies. Came home
took a nap before
supper.
7-6-00. It was back

to Sue's at 10:00.
Day went better.
We still took a nap
when we got home.
7-7-00 We finished
mailing at Sue's
today.
Came home did our
usual nap routine.
Went to Chenese resta-
urant for supper.
7-8-00 Finished putting
the cross stitch box
together. I've made this
for a door prize at
Berkey-Robinson reunion.
This evening we had
our annual dinner
at Trayers. ~~All to~~ Mike
+ Pat Rawls also join us.
These are Dometic
employees that Max
keeps in touch with.
We always have a very
good time together.
7-9-00 Today was our
day out with Danny.
We took him to Grand

Prix go cart races at
So Bend airport.
We used their van
with the new lift
installed. That worked
very good.
We had a fun day.
We came home this
evening and collapsed.
Those lazy boy chairs
sure feel good.
7-10-00 It rained off + on
all day.
I played with
computer. Got
frustrated. And finally
quit.
Didn't accomplish
much else today.
7-11-00 Had lunch with
Dick + Esther today.
Dick took me on tour
of the internet. Very
intelligent man.
7-12-00 - No place to go
today. So we worked.
Got trailer all clean.
Windows too.

Sure glad that job is over for awhile.

7-13-00 May & I had lunch with Lola today.

We were very impressed with the quality of service in the dining room.

Then after lunch I put her pictures in an album for her. She appreciated it so much.

7-14-00 We stayed put today.

May washed truck. We are getting so clean it's scary.

7-15-00 Went to breakfast with some class mate from high school this morning.

Came home and took the rest of the day off.

7-16-00 Drove to Syracuse Lake today.

We stopped at Smeltzer

Cottage and the man living next door in Uncle John's old cottage invited us in to see how it looked now. Couldn't really tell that it was the cottage as for the Smeltzer cottage it needs to be torn down. Janice Smeltzer son now owns it. He just mows the lawn.

Came home and hooked up to some free time on AOL.

So many things I can do with this computer. 7-17-00 I went to lunch with Marilyn @ Olive Garden. Sherry Houghton and daughter joined us there.

We then went to Sherry's house. They planned their trip to Colorado. After that we took a swim.

Max helped Sue with getting Mulch. We met back at Sue's, got groceries, and came home.

That was Plenty for one day.

7-18-00 Our days are busy lately. We went to Sue's and washed, worked on a slide presentation. This took us all day.

Came home and collapsed.

7-19-00 Another busy day. Went to funeral home this PM. Bill Simms, passed away. A friend. — Then finished getting ready for Tim's Bday. Went to Bock's this evening. Celebrated Tim's 40TH.

Came home fell asleep in chair.

7-20-00 We took our time getting around

this morning. After lunch we moved to Miller's for Berkey-Robinson Reunion. Had a nice visit with Char and family.

7-21 · 7-24 -

We laughed, enjoyed, ate and a little bit more with the group at the reunion. Sun eve the 23rd we crashed in our trailer. On Monday the 24th Max dropped me off at Sue's house and he took trailer to get brakes repaired. Terry & family were staying at Sue's. Sue & Tim were on vacation for a couple days by themselves.

We came on home and got trailer set up. Late afternoon they stopped by. We all went to dinner at Hacienda.

7-25-00 - Today was Sr. Citizen day at fair. We took advantage of it.

Got to fair about 3:30. Saw Terry + family + Danney + Iris.

They had been there since noon and about ready to leave.

We did our usual walk around and then ate and went to grandstand about 5:30 PM. Its free so you have to get there early. Show starts at 7:30 PM. Lorrie Morgan was on. She is a favorite country singer of Max and I. We enjoyed the show.

7-26-00. We were back to a slower pace today. Just stayed home.

7-27-00 Max + Sue went to tractor pull. This is their annual day out.

I stayed with Danny & Iris.

I came home about 6:30.

Max and Sue came home at midnight. - Oh, I found out it was 1:00 A.M.

7-28-00

Max was tired from tractor pull & slept in til 10:15.

This P.M. we stayed at Sue's with D & I then went to Bob Evans for supper & grocery store that is enough for one day.

7-29-00 We had our annual visit with Ron & Gloria Hammon this eve. They sure would like doing what we do. as a life style.

Had a pleasant evening

7-30-00 Max and I both played lazy all

*day Today.

7-31-00 We were up
bright and early this
morn. I had appointments
at clinic at 4:00 & 9:30.
We came home and
worked on slide out
awning.

Max got it already
to go up. - That will be
another day.

8-1-00 - Had to go back
to clinic for blood test -
Both of us.

Then we went to Sue's.
She & I went shopping
at UP Mall. We hadn't
had a day out this
summer.

It was so nice to
go with my daughter
again.

Max stayed with Danny
& Iris.

Came home & collapsed
this evening.

8-2-00 - Max got the
slide-out awning on

today. Shorty helped him.

I worked on projects in trailer.

8-3-00 - didn't accomplish much today. Just stayed home.

8-4-00 Worked on picture book once again. This is my history book. Don't know if I will ever get it organized.

Went to Sue's and Max helped Jim start the project of putting in a new door.

8-5-00 Stayed home today. Worked a little more on my history picture album. Max was into a race.

Need to call a few more people to do things with. before we leave.

8-6-00 A fun morning. We took Sue & family to breakfast at Mayberry Cafe. This was in celebration of their 20th anniversary. While at the restaurant we saw 2 families of old neighbors. The Croughs & McClures.

We came back to their house & checked out changes to trailer. The reason for changes so Danny can go camping and maneuver in trailer. Looks like its going to work.

We came home and I worked some more on my history photo album.

8-7-00 I worked with my scanner today. Seems my progress is very slow. But, I'm getting there.

Max did some maint-ainence work outside.

8-8-00 - I progressed a

bit more with my scanner. Someday I might understand.

8-9-00. Got a much needed hair cut today. Then, went to network land for a computer class regarding my scanner.

I'll conquer that thing yet.

8-10-00. It was up and on the go again today.

We stayed with Danny & Iris.

Sue was at a retreat for school. Tim was at Purdue for a job interview.

We took them to Wendy's in Goshen. Actually we took our food to Shanklin park and had our lunch.

Then we took a walk at the park

Max cooked pork chops for dinner and I fixed their favorite cheezy potatoes for supper.

Jim got home about the time we were finished.

He had been offered a new job. He was so excited. He told us all about it.

We came home and collapsed.

8-11-00 Max made his annual trip to DTI this morning.

I stayed home and got a bundle of things done.

This afternoon we went to RV show at Notre Dame.

That was a worthless trip.

If you don't want a $250,000 motor home or 40' 5th wheel forget it.

8-12-00 - This was Sue, Iris and my annual day at Amish Acres Art Festival. We left about 10:30 and didn't get home until 6:00. We had a very fun enjoyable day.

It was hot but we rested in shade once in awile. All in all we had a great day!

8-13-00 - After 3 busy days, we just took the easy way out and stayed put today.

8-14-00 Sure did lots of brain work today. Trying to find out if we will continue with AOL or not.

Also did a picture attached to E-Mail. That was challenging. So far so good.

8-15-00 - Got my hair done again. Gee I'm back on a weekly

schedule.

Nothing much exciting going on.

We just got things around in anticipation of our move tomorrow.

8-16-00 We moved on to Terry's area today. Max stopped at Angola interchange to adjust ~~breaks~~ brakes.

We got to the different campground about 3:15 our time. This is Green Valley CG. We are trying it out this year.

Went to visit Elle & Jon and family this evening.

The kids are always excited when we get there.

8-17-00 This was a busy fun day.

About noon we went to Robinson house. I washed a couple

loads of clothes.
Jon, Elle & I made
candy cane cookies.
Getting Jon not to
eat all of dough
was quite a trick.
But we had fun.
Played a few wild
games of ~~Yatzee~~ 50.
Terry never did get
home to see us.
We left at 9:30 P.M.
Another long day for
him.
8-18-00 - Terry came home
at noon today.
We just stayed at
their house.
8-19-00 Terry took us
to Henry Ford - Greenfield
Village. They had a new
round house - railroad
exhibit open.
Watched some glass
blowing, took a train
ride. We all got ice
cream and headed
home.

We grilled out, I mean Terry cooked over grill.

We headed to trailer. Very tired.

8-20-22 We kept very busy while in Novi.

Jon & Elle stayed overnight on Sunday.

We had a fun day at trailer.

Mon late afternoon we took them home.

Jon had a birthday overnight.

I stayed at Terry's so I could be there Tues when he came home.

Elle & I played games.

Tues night we took Elle to soccer practice. Jeanette took Jon.

Finally met up and had pizza for supper.

We said our good-byes

and went back to
trailer.

8-23-00 We headed back
to Goshen.

Had a good time but
good to slow down
again.

8-24-00 We both got
hair appointments out
of the way today.
We were at Sue's for
supper.

Came home tired once
again. Just haven't
caught up yet.

8-25-00 I had lunch with
Monali Daas from
the bank.

So few people left
there that I know.

This evening we started
festivites for May's 50th
High School class
reunion.

First we went to
High School football
game.

Then it was onto

Elks club for
hors de vours. And
social time.
Lots of people to see
and try and remember
who they were.
Came home collapsed
once again.
Max did alot of
reminising when he
got home.
I went to bed. I was
tired.
8-26-00 Going again today.
First stop was S Ray.
Miller Auto Museum.
Just Max & I stopped at
Mayberry Cafe.
Came back home, got
a nap before the
big evening festivities.
At 5:30 we left for (Class
of 50 dinner at Elks)
Club. We got our
pictures taken,
socialized, had dinner
and a very nice program.
This was the nicest class

reunion we've been to.
But when it's the
50th it should be.
8-27-00 - Whew! Guess
we were tired. Didn't
make it up in time
to go to class of 50
breakfast.
We just stayed put
all day.
8-28-00 I spent most of
my day on the
computer. My time is
running out that I
will have a phone
hook up everyday so I'm
trying to take advantage
of that.
8-29-00 Needed groceries
bad.
May has serious
cold.
I did some running
around and got groceries.
Also trying to use my
time online while I
still have phone hooked
up.

8-30-00 - Had our annual meeting with financial advisor. Things look good in that respect. This P.M. I was back to working on picture book.

9-1-00 - Slept in this morning. Max still battling his cold. After School Iris came to stay with us overnight. She got to swim a long time.

9-2-00 We took Iris to breakfast at old bag factory in Goshen, went thru the shops and came back to trailer and she & I went swimming.

Max went back to chiropractor for his sore neck.

We played some games

and went swimming
again & again.
Marilyn stopped
by.
Then we took Iris
home after she
left.
We came home and
took it easy tonight.
9-3-00 - We were at Sue's
by 9:45. We went with
her family to So Bend
Regional Airport to the
Abate Ride for MDA.
Father, Sue & I rode
in a red 57 chevy.
Iris & Tim rode in
another 57 chevy.
(Of course, Danny the
star of our show was
in a motorcycle side
car.
After an 1½ hour ride
we came back to
airport area and had
lunch.
Iris rode home with
us to go swimming

The pool was closed.

We went back to their house later.

I stayed over night so I'd be there when Sue & Tim left early to go to work at MDA telethon at Pierre Moran. Danny, Iris, Max & I went at 9:30 AM.

We thought we'd get a break to come back home. But, we didn't. We stayed until time to go to WSJV studios. for the big presentation by Abate. They raised $147,000+ from the ride. The total from region 1 was $60,000+.

We stayed on another half hour til the finish of telethon.

We came back to their house.

We packed up laundry & came home.

We were 2 tired grandparents. We just collapsed.

In some small way we helped and that was a good feeling.

9-5-00 - This was a much slower pace day. Slept in, paid bills & got a few groceries. Weather was cooler. Fall is in the air. We are really getting ready to fly south.

9-6-00 - Kinda a slow day. I did some computer projects. Max worked on a map project. He was drawing where we have been in the US. in 6 yrs.

Mornings are cooler now. We've turned on heater the last 2 mornings. Fall is in the air.

9-7-00 We drove to Argos today to visit

our friend Mary Davis.

It's always fun to visit with her but it was also kinda sad, Herm passed away last yr.

9-8-00 Cleaned house today.

We went with friends Lee & Verba Prough, our first neighbors.

We met them at Appleby's and then came back and visited at trailer.

9-9-00 I did a little shopping on my own. Came home - watched a lot of sports. Football is in full swing.

My printer is giving me a few problems so I worked with that this evening. Solved nothing but I will get it.

9-10-00 - We got much needed rain today. We did go to Bob Evans for breakfast.

The rest of the day we stayed put and watched some sports. I did get most of my computer problems solved. I have just one problem out of 4 unsolved.

9-11-00 This was my day out to celebrate with Marilyn, her birthday.

Max took me there, then she & I went to Cheese Cake Cafe. Never had been there. We had lunch and then did some shopping at Big K Mart then came back across town and went to our favorite store "Kohls."

Of course we found

something to buy there.

9-12-00 Jammed a lot in today.

Downtown to bank, got a perm.

Groceries, went to Sue's, washed clothes there, got supper there. I'm so tired time we got home.

It was our last get together for the summer.

9-13-00 Very tired today but we did get things picked up & put away.

Defrosted refrigerator.

9-14-00 - Today is leaving day.

The park manager Loren was sorry to see Max go.

It's always hard leaving family.

But it's time to move on for winter months.

Once on the road it got easier.

9-15-00 - I thought I had avoided May's cold but today I'm starting it, I feel lousey.

I did make it to club house to down load computer. That worked O.K.

I did have some problem getting some info Max wanted. He thinks I can perform miracles and just find it. Well, I didn't.

I'm sure Richard can help me out.

Stayed put tonight and watched opening ceremonies of Olympics.

9-16-00 - A beautiful day outside. Me with cold and blahs inside. Good thing there is football & olympics on TV. But, I sleep thru parts of it. I will get better.

9-17-00 - Still feeling kinda punk with my cold.

Just not moving very quickly.

I did manage to get us breakfast and a shower by noon.

Continued watching Olympics.

Max is doing good with his walking

I'm way behind with that.

9-18-00 The fall kind of weather that I enjoy is here.

Feeling a little better today. We made it to town for lunch & groceries.

Plus a little computer work and out door time.

9-19-00 Max got a big spurt of energy and washed truck & trailer.

I worked on things

inside).

9-20-00 Finally got at picture book once again. Still have some to put in but trying to catch up.

9-21-00 Got washing done today along with trip to town for a few things.

Seems like we were on the go all day. This cold still draining and giving me fits. Max flew kite once again.

9-22-00 Moved on to Rick & Teresa's this morning. Will be there three week-end. Teresa was home today when we arrived. We got backed in on her drive before she knew we were there.

Rick arrived home at 5:00. Had dinner with them in their

very beautiful home.
9-23-00 Started off with breakfast. fit for king & queen.

Then Rick held class for us on computer I call this Ricks 101 Computer Class. We went about 3 hours. Took a drive late afternoon. It started to rain. We didn't make it to October fest.

Stopped at a Christmas store instead. Came home for a little bit and then met her parents, Bill & Martha at a restaurant for dinner. Came home & Rick had some more computer class for Martha & I. Then, we watched some Olympic's and went to bed.

Fun filled day but

very tired.

9-24-00 Rick helped me with more computer knowledge. Pretty much stayed put at their house. Rained off & on all day.

9-25-00 We said our good byes to Rick last night.

Had breakfast with Teresa.

We packed up and headed south.

Just got out of Dayton and it began to rain. It was miserable.

We had a good week end but both were tired.

We drove to Mammoth Cave area, found an RPI park and will stay 3 nights.

Tomorrow we will stay put at trailer & rest.

9-26-00 We did stay put today. Took

a couple walks and that was it.

9-27-00 We explored a cave at Mammoth Cave today. Although it was in Mammoth Cave National Park, it was not a part of Mammoth cave. At least they have not discovered the connecting passage yet. It was called Great Onyx cave.

After lunch we took a River Cruise on Green River. Just a beautiful fall day to look at nature.

9-28-00 We moved to Beech Bend Park @ Bowling Green Ky. Only a 40 minute drive. After we got set up, went to post office, got tires rotated, had lunch and came back home. Enough for 1 day

9-29-00 We are having the

beautiful fall weather.
We went to Corvette Car
Factory at 1:00 for tour.
I was wiped out by
time we got done
here.

Max decided he would
go to stock car race
tonight. It was in
complex of campground.
I stayed home worked
on little things &
rested.

9-30-00 Max enjoyed his
races.

Our day out today took
us to Corvette.

Just stayed home
today.

10-1-00 - I went with
Max to drag races here
at Beech Bend Complex.
Never been to these
before. But, we packed
up our cooler & cushions
and away we went.
Not the most exciting
thing I've ever

done. But OK for 1 afternoon in my life time.

10-2-00 We toured the National Corvette Museum today. Got Danny a shirt as part of his Christmas present. Called Elle. She will be 9 yrs old tomorrow. She was very excited.

10-3-00 Did a shopping oil change, barber shop run today.

Should have that kind of stuff taken care of for awhile.

Went to laundry, where I could plug computer in to phone. That went OK. First time I've done that.

10-4-00 Went to laundry area to hook up modem. You'd have thought I was a teacher another lady & her husband were questioning me.

Turned out they had just got their laptop in June also. This laundry area is not a good set up but it worked. Went back in afternoon and did laundry.

10-5-00 Movin on down the road today I-65 was so busy with trucks. Sure glad I wasn't driving.

Anyway we arrived at Cages Bend Corps of Engineers Park at Gallatin Key.

This is a very pretty park on Old Hickory Lake and the sites are big.

10-6-00 We started out for the information center in Nashville just off I-65. Wrong they moved it to downtown. So plan B came into plan. We picked up our tickets at Grand Ole Opry.

Then proceeded across the street to Opry Mills. Opry Mills replaced Opryland. Its a humangous mall with everything in it. Its so big. Maybe we saw a 1/3 of it.

Found a TGI Friday restaurant and had lunch. Stopped at a Ghiradelli Choc store. I splurged and bought a couple candy bars so I could have a bite in future. Sinful but good.

Came home and got a much needed nap.

10-7-00 Cold out today. A cold front has come thru. We plan to stay put anyway. This is Sat and a day we watch football.

I worked on my

Computer alot. I'm making Halloween cards for grandkids. Sometimes I have trouble doing what I want the computer to do. Dumb Computer.

10-8-00 - Weather cooler today. Kind of a repeat of yesterday. Worked on Halloween Cards, watched football & stayed put. Thats ok need these kind of days sometimes.

10-9-00 Finished up Halloween Cards today. Also completed anniv. card for T & J.
Went to town of Gallatin TN. Got lunch there plus some groceries. and came home.
Finally caught up with talking to Sue.

10-10-00 Nice Day. We drove to Country Music Hall of Fame.

We thought they had built a new one. Ended up the building is in progress and won't open til 5/01. We toured the old one anyway. It really needs to be updated. After that we went to downtown area.

We ate a Fuddruckers Restaurant. Nothing fancy. I ordered a garden chicken salad. It was huge. I could have fed 4-6 people after on that salad. Needless to say I didn't eat it all.

We walked around downtown area. Then went back to truck & came home.

10-11-00 What a fall day! We stayed out and enjoyed the out of doors (cooked out, walked and just sat outside).

I did start working on
my challenge of the
scanner.

10-12-00 We made our
trip to Opryland Hotel
for lunch. And took
a walk thru to see
all their Plantings.
It is one unbelievable
atrium.

10-13-00 Received a
big bag of mail today.
Sat outside and
worked on it.
Such nice fall
weather.

10-14-00 This was our
day to see the Grande
Ole Opry 75th Anniversary
With tickets in hand we
were off to the Matinee.
We saw Steve Warner,
Porter Wagoner, ~~Hance Hel~~
Garth Brooks Trisha
Yearwood, Travis Tritt
and Loretta Lynn.
Really a good show
afterwards we saw ✍

Lorrie Morgan & Loretta Lynn arrive for the celebrity walk of stars. A fun day. No football this day.

10-15-00 Worked with my scanner this A.M. Haven't got things all figured out on this yet. Maybe someday. I gave up and took a walk to clear my head.

10-16-00 Moved on to Decatur Alabama today. Staying at Point Mallard Campground for 2 nights. Finally got back to working on picture books this P.M. Got to catch up.

10-17-00 We explored Decatur today. It seems that the streets went every way but sensful. But, we found our way around

10-18-00 Movin on to a corps of Engineer Park near Montgomery Al. Found a beautiful campsite on river at Gunter C.G. The weather a perfect fall day. Quite secluded too.

10-19-00 – A Happy Day – My birthday. Weather was perfect.

We stayed put and enjoyed our day at campground.

Max even tried fishing. The only bad thing about it, at this beautiful campsite is that we are attacked every evening by young mosquitos. The last 2 nights we have spent try to kill them. There have been lots of them. A man in the campground gave us some fish. Max cleaned them and we will have them over the weekend.

Well I've moved on to age 66 now. Can't believe it.

10-20-00 - Moved on to SKP PARK - Plantation at Foley, Al. near the gulf of mexico.

Even got a little rain the last 30 miles or so. Rain is needed so badly. Went to Social hour. People are very friendly in this park.

We will stay put a week or 2 here.

10-21-00 We continue to keep ourselves busy. Sometimes I think too busy.

But, we got to post office, got groceries, got computer hooked in to AOL for phone #800 - and managed to watch football, golf & baseball. Plus we talked to family in Detroit. Sue and family are there for weekend.

10-22-00 Our weather is continuing to stay warm. 80°. Got caught up in a ton of laundry today.

The world series is going on. Yankees are ahead of Mets. 2 games to one.

10-23-00 This was a go play day. We drove to ocean at Gulf Shores. I should say Gulf of Mexico.

Took our lunch, chairs and a kite.

We flew kites, sat on beach had our lunch and walked the beach. Drove around Gulf Shores and came home.

10-24-00 This was a finish up projects day. Completed absentee ballot and finished up Halloween Cards for kids. Enough work done. Max did his running to get oil & hg etc.

10-25-00 We drove the scenic route along Mobile Bay thru Fairhope AL and then stopped at a favorite restaurant near Mobile AL. The restaurant was the Nautilus. This is where we had my birthday lunch.

10-26-00 Went to a computer class this evening. Not what I expected. But did pick up a few pointers.

Yankees won series tonight.

10-27-00 Made reservations to fly home for Christmas. Also got reservations for campgrounds down the road.

Then we drove to Perdido Bay and into Florida. Walked the white sandy beaches again. Enjoyable day.

10-28-00 Stayed put today. Worked on mail we had just received.

10-29-00 Went to breakfast in Gulf Shores, overlooking Gulf of Mexico.

Tonight worked on computer. Messed up my printer.

10-30-00 Got my printer fixed all by myself.